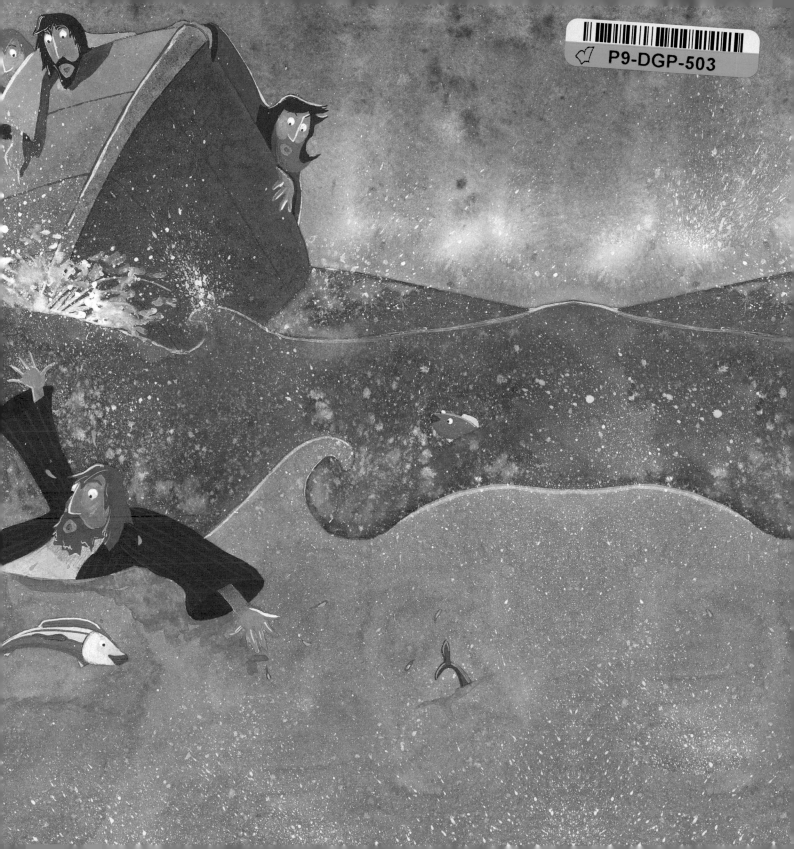
P9-DGP-503

This book belongs to

....

....

My BIBLE STORIES Treasury

Retold by
**Mary Batchelor
and Penny Boshoff**

make
believe
ideas

Copyright © 2020

make believe ideas ltd

The Wilderness, Berkhamsted, Hertfordshire, HP4 2AZ, UK.
501 Nelson Place, P.O. Box 141000, Nashville, TN 37214-1000, USA.

Retold by Mary Batchelor and Penny Boshoff.
Some of the material contained in this book previously
appeared in *My First Bedtime Bible* © 2005 make believe ideas ltd.,
My First Read-Aloud Bible © 2009 make believe ideas ltd,
and *5 Minute Bible Stories* © 2017 make believe ideas ltd.

Illustrated by Sara Baker and Nikki Loy.

Additional illustrations by Jo Goodberry,
Helen Parrott, and Cathy Shimmen.

ISBN: 978-1-80058-070-1

All rights reserved. No part of this publication may be
reproduced, stored in a retrieval system, or transmitted
in any form or by any means, electronic, mechanical,
photocopying, recording, or otherwise, without the
prior written permission of the copyright owner.
Recommended for children aged 3 years and over.
Manufactured in China.
www.makebelieveideas.com

Contents

The Old Testament 7
The New Testament 130
Index 254

Old Testament Stories

Making our world	8	God sends food	50	A temple for God	92
God fills the world	10	God gives water	52	Elijah and the bad king	94
Adam and Eve	12	Rules for the people	54	The real God	96
Forbidden fruit	14	Reaching Canaan	56	Elijah and Elisha	98
Cain and Abel	16	Brave Rahab	58	One bottle of oil	100
Noah and the flood	18	The walls fall down	60	Naaman is healed	102
Rainbow in the sky	20	Gideon	62	King Joash	104
God chooses Abraham	22	Samson's riddle	64	Jonah and the big fish	106
Three strangers	24	Samson and the Philistines	66	God forgives	108
Isaac	26	Naomi and Ruth	68	A lost book is found	110
Esau and Jacob	28	A happy ending	70	Jeremiah is rescued	112
Jacob's dream	30	God answers a prayer	72	Leaving Jerusalem	114
Joseph's coat	32	God calls Samuel	74	Daniel	116
Joseph goes to Egypt	34	King of Israel	76	Saved from the fire	118
Joseph saves Egypt	36	Saul disobeys God	78	Daniel and the lions	120
Brothers reunited	38	A new king	80	Queen Esther	122
Moses	40	David and Goliath	82	Esther saves the Jews	124
Fire in the bush	42	David and Jonathan	84	Rebuilding Jerusalem	126
Moses warns the king	44	Saul chases David	86	Give thanks to God	128
Chaos in Egypt	46	David becomes king	88		
The waves roll back	48	Wise Solomon	90		

Making our world

Long ago, when God began to make everything, the earth was dark and empty.

God said, "Earth needs light." And light appeared. God made the sun to shine by day and the moon and stars to light the night.

God was pleased with what he had done.

DEAR GOD, THANK YOU FOR MAKING OUR BEAUTIFUL WORLD. AMEN.

God fills the world

THANK YOU, GOD, FOR ALL THE DIFFERENT BIRDS AND ANIMALS AND FOR THE SOUNDS THEY MAKE. AMEN.

God said, "I will make grass and flowers and trees to cover Earth."

Then he made all kinds of creatures. He made fish to swim in the rivers and seas, birds and butterflies to fill the air, and animals, big and small, to play on the land.

What sorts of big and small animals live near you?

Adam and Eve

God wanted someone to love. So he made Adam and Eve to be his friends and to take care of his Earth.

"Enjoy the fruit in my garden," said God. Then he pointed to one tree. "But don't eat fruit from that tree. If you do, you will die."

Adam and Eve were very happy in God's garden.

What plants and animals can you see in the garden?

THANK YOU, GOD, FOR MAKING PEOPLE AND FOR MAKING ME. AMEN.

Forbidden fruit

The fruit on the forbidden tree looked delicious. "Why not try it?" the snake asked. "But God said we would die," said Eve.

"Don't listen to God," the snake whispered.

DEAR GOD, I'M SORRY FOR SOMETIMES BEING DISOBEDIENT. PLEASE FORGIVE ME. AMEN.

So Eve picked some and shared it with Adam.

God was sad that they had disobeyed him. Now Adam and Eve had to leave God's garden.

Why do you think Adam and Eve ate the fruit?

Cain and Abel

Adam and Eve had two sons: Cain and Abel. Cain thought that God loved Abel more than him. So he hated his brother more and more.

Why should we try to get along with our brothers and sisters?

One day, when they were out in the fields, Cain killed Abel.

God was very sad. Hate and murder were spoiling his Earth. Cain had to leave home and move far away.

DEAR GOD, HELP ME NOT TO BE JEALOUS OF OTHER CHILDREN. AMEN.

Noah and the flood

Nobody on Earth listened to God—except Noah. "Noah, there's going to be a flood," said God. "Build a big boat for your family. And take two of every kind of animal and bird with you."

Noah did what God told him.
Then it rained and rained.
Water covered the land,
but Noah's boat floated safely.

How did Noah know to build a big boat?

PLEASE, GOD, KEEP US SAFE, TOO.
AMEN.

Rainbow in the sky

At last the rain stopped. When the land was dry, Noah opened the door. Out flew the birds, off scampered the animals and Noah said a special thank you to God.

"Noah," said God, "when you see the rainbow, remember my promise: I will never flood the whole earth again."

God chooses Abraham

Abraham and Sarah longed for a baby. One day, God said, "Abraham, I've chosen you. So leave your house and take your tent. We're going on a journey.

"I will give you a new land and a big family. Everyone in the whole world will be happy because of you and your family."

Why do you think God chose Abraham? What sort of person do you think he was?

THANK YOU, DEAR GOD, THAT WE ARE
ALL SPECIAL TO YOU. AMEN.

Three strangers

One hot day Abraham saw three tired strangers. "Come and rest here!" he called.

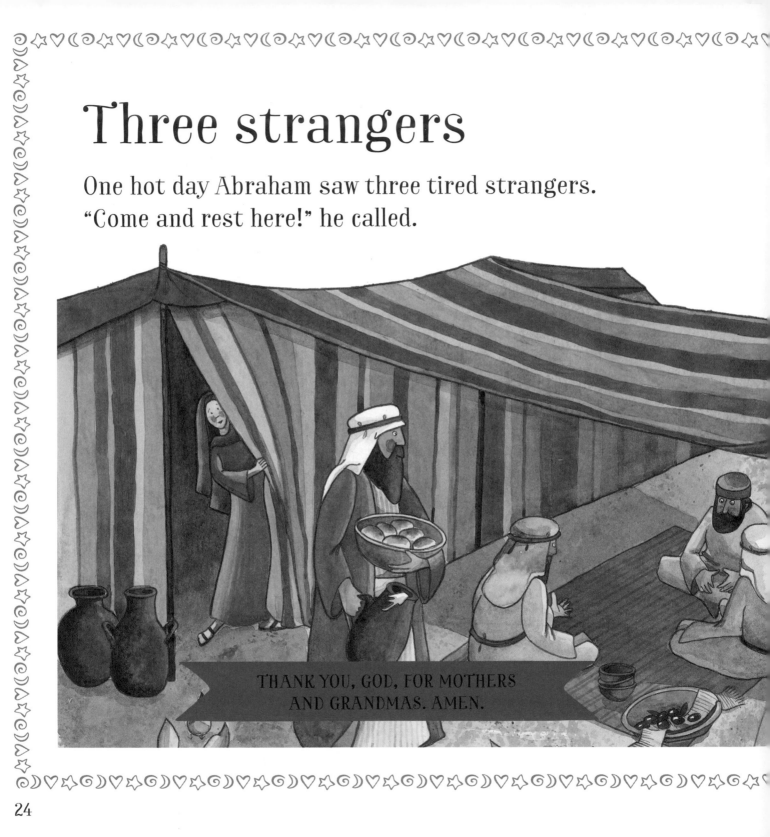

THANK YOU, GOD, FOR MOTHERS AND GRANDMAS. AMEN.

Do you think God was pleased that Abraham offered the strangers food and rest? Why?

So they sat in the shade while Abraham brought them food and water. He didn't guess that they were God's messengers. "Next year Sarah will have a baby boy," they said.

Isaac

God kept his promise
and baby Isaac was born.

Some years later, God said,
"Abraham, will you give Isaac back to me?"

But just as Abraham was getting ready
to give Isaac back, God called out,
"Abraham, I know now how much you love
and trust me. I won't take Isaac away."

How did God find out that Abraham truly trusted him?

HELP ME, GOD, TO TRUST YOU ALWAYS,
NO MATTER WHAT. AMEN.

Esau and Jacob

Isaac married Rebekah and they had twin sons: Esau and Jacob. One day, Esau arrived back from hunting. Jacob was cooking delicious food.

"Give me some!" cried Esau.
"I'm starving!"

DEAR GOD, HELP ME TO BE FAIR
TO OTHERS. AMEN.

"Only if you give me your special place as eldest son," said Jacob.

"All right!" Esau agreed.

Do you think this was a fair swap? Why?

Jacob's dream

Jacob tricked Esau again. Esau wanted
to kill Jacob, so Jacob ran away.
That night Jacob slept under the stars.

THANK YOU, GOD, FOR BEING WITH US
ALL NIGHT LONG. AMEN.

In his dream he saw a staircase. Angels were going up and down.

Then God said, "Jacob, I promise to be with you. I'll never leave you. You and your family will have the good things I promised to Abraham."

Where do you think the staircase might lead to?

Joseph's coat

Jacob had lots of children but Joseph was his favorite. He gave Joseph a beautiful coat. Joseph's brothers were jealous.

HELP ME, DEAR GOD,
TO ALWAYS BE KIND. AMEN.

One day, Joseph went to the fields to find his brothers.

How would you feel if someone was given a special coat, but not you?

"Let's get him," the brothers cried. They grabbed Joseph, ripped off his special coat, and threw him down an empty well.

Joseph goes to Egypt

The brothers decided to sell Joseph to some men traveling to Egypt.

In Egypt, Joseph became Potiphar's slave.

Because Joseph worked so hard, Potiphar put him in charge of everything he had.

But Potiphar's wife told lies about Joseph, so he was sent to prison. Even there, God was still with him.

Who was mean to Joseph, and who was kind to him?

HELP ME, DEAR GOD, NOT TO TELL LIES ABOUT OTHER CHILDREN. AMEN.

Joseph saves Egypt

The king of Egypt had worrying dreams.
"Fetch Joseph," a servant said.
"He understands dreams."

The king told Joseph his dream.
"God says seven good harvests are
coming, followed by seven bad ones,"
Joseph explained. "Save food now to
feed your people in the bad years."

The king was pleased. "Joseph,
you must help me lead Egypt."

DEAR GOD, PLEASE HELP ME
TO HAVE GOOD DREAMS. AMEN.

Brothers reunited

Now Joseph's brothers had to travel to Egypt to buy corn. They did not know that the man in charge was Joseph. Joseph pretended to be angry.

DEAR GOD, HELP ME TO BE
FORGIVING LIKE JOSEPH. AMEN.

Then he said, "Don't be frightened. It's me, Joseph! I will take care of you. God brought me here to save everyone! Come and live in Egypt."

Had Joseph forgiven his brothers? How can you tell?

Moses

God gave Jacob the name "Israel." Israel's people stayed in Egypt. But years later, a cruel king made them his slaves.

"Kill all their baby boys!" he ordered. But one mother hid her baby in a floating basket among the river reeds.

"What's in that basket?" asked the princess. Her servant opened the lid.

"What a beautiful baby!" the princess exclaimed.
"I shall keep him and name him Moses."

How did baby Moses survive?

PLEASE, GOD, TAKE CARE OF BABIES.
AMEN.

Fire in the bush

When Moses grew up he longed
to save his people. The king was
furious, so Moses ran far away.

One day, Moses saw a bush on fire.
"That's strange!" he thought.

Suddenly God spoke from the bush.
"Moses, go back to Egypt and
rescue your unhappy people."

"I can't!" Moses exclaimed.
"Yes, you can," God said,
"because I will be with you."

Why do you think
Moses said
"I can't!" to God?

THANK YOU, DEAR GOD, FOR ALWAYS
BEING WITH US. AMEN.

Moses warns the king

Moses set off for Egypt.
"God says you must
let his people go,"
he told the king.

PLEASE HELP ME, GOD, TO
BE OBEDIENT. AMEN.

44

"NO!" the king replied. "I don't know or care about your God. I won't let them go. Make the Israelites work harder!"

"Obey God or bad things will happen," Moses warned. "I won't!" the king replied.

Do you think Moses was brave to stand up to the king?

Chaos in Egypt

Everything happened as Moses had warned. First frogs ran everywhere, then flies came, then there were storms. But still the king would not let the Israelites go.

THANK YOU, GOD, FOR KEEPING YOUR PEOPLE SAFE. AMEN.

"God will rescue his people," Moses said, "but because of you, Egypt will be sad."

"Go away!" the king shouted.

Should the king have listened to Moses? Why?

"Tomorrow God will rescue us," Moses told the Israelites. "Cook a special meal to thank him."

The waves roll back

The next day the Israelites left Egypt and camped by the Red Sea. But the Egyptian army chased them!

God said, "Moses, stretch your stick over the sea. Tell the people to go forward."

Moses obeyed God. The waters rolled back and the Israelites crossed on dry ground.

"Hurrah!" they shouted on the other side. "God has rescued us!"

How did the Israelites get to the other side of the Red Sea?

DEAR GOD, THANK YOU FOR RESCUING THE ISRAELITES. AMEN.

God sends food

"God is leading us to the country
he promised us," Moses told the Israelites
as they walked through the desert.

"There's nothing to eat!"
the people grumbled.
"I will feed you every day,"
God promised.

THANK YOU, GOD, FOR OUR FOOD EACH DAY.
AMEN.

The next morning the ground was covered with small white flakes. They tasted good, like honey cookies.

Why weren't the Israelites happy to be free at first?

God gives water

The people kept grumbling. "We're thirsty, Moses," they moaned. "Give us water!"

Moses told God and God said, "Go to the special rock that I will show you and hit it with your stick."

Moses did as God told him and cool, refreshing water gushed from the rock. There was plenty for everyone.

How did the Israelites get food and water in the desert?

THANK YOU, DEAR GOD, FOR CLEAN WATER. AMEN.

Rules for the people

God said to Moses, "These rules will help my people every day: Put me first and love me best. Don't worship anyone but me. Don't use my name carelessly. Keep one day each week as a resting day with me.

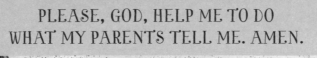

PLEASE, GOD, HELP ME TO DO
WHAT MY PARENTS TELL ME. AMEN.

"Obey your father and mother. Don't hurt others. Keep love between a husband and wife special. Don't take what isn't yours. Don't tell lies about other people. Don't be jealous of other people and want what they have."

Do you think these rules are still important today? Why?

Reaching Canaan

When they reached the land God had promised them, Moses sent twelve spies to look around.

"It's a wonderful country," the spies said, "but we'll never win it! The people there are huge and strong!" But Caleb and Joshua shouted out, "God will help us!" And he did.

Do you think the people believed God would help them win the land?

DEAR GOD, HELP ME WHEN I DON'T KNOW WHAT TO DO. AMEN.

Brave Rahab

When Moses died, God made Joshua the leader. Joshua sent two spies to Jericho. The king sent soldiers to seize them, but Rahab hid them.

DEAR GOD, PLEASE HELP ME
TO BE BRAVE. AMEN.

Finally the soldiers left. Rahab said to the spies: "When God gives you Jericho, please be kind to me."

"We will!" they promised.

Where did Rahab hide the spies?

The walls fall down

Joshua did everything God told him.

So for six days, Joshua and the soldiers and priests marched once around Jericho. On the seventh day they marched around seven times, blowing their trumpets.

Then everyone shouted. At once, the walls of the city fell. CRASH! But Rahab was not hurt.

Why was Rahab protected when the walls came down?

PLEASE HELP ME, GOD, TO DO EVERYTHING
THAT YOU TELL ME TO DO. AMEN.

Gideon

THANK YOU, GOD, FOR RESCUING US.
AMEN.

How do you think God would have felt when the Israelites forgot about him?

The Israelites soon forgot God. But God did not forget them.

When enemies attacked Israel, God said to Gideon, "Rescue my people. I'll show you how!"

That night Gideon and his soldiers crept to the enemy camp with trumpets and jars with torches inside.

At Gideon's signal, every soldier smashed his jar, blew his trumpet, and shouted, "For God and for Gideon!"

And Israel's enemies ran away!

Samson's riddle

Enemies attacked Israel and God chose strong Samson to fight them. Samson told his enemies this riddle: "Out of the eater came something to eat. Out of the strong came something sweet."

His enemies, the Philistines, were puzzled. Then they discovered that Samson had found a bee's nest in a lion's dead body and he'd eaten the delicious honey.

What was the eater? What was the thing it ate?

DEAR GOD, THANK YOU FOR
THE FOOD WE EAT. AMEN.

Samson and the Philistines

HELP ME, GOD, NOT TO BULLY OTHERS.
AMEN.

Finally the Philistines caught Samson. They blinded him and brought him to their temple.

"Our god Dagon is the greatest!" they shouted.

"God, please help me to beat the Philistines," Samson prayed.

He put his hands on the big pillars and pushed and pushed. Crack. CRASH!

The temple fell down and killed everyone. Samson was remembered as a great hero.

Naomi and Ruth

Naomi's family lived in Bethlehem. But when the food ran out, they moved to far-away Moab.

Poor Naomi! Her husband and sons died. But their Moabite wives, Orpah and Ruth, looked after her.

"I'm going back to Bethlehem," Naomi said. "Good bye," said Orpah, hugging Naomi.

But Ruth said, "I'm coming with you. I'll stay with you always. I love you and your God will be my God."

Do you think it would have been hard for Ruth to move countries?

THANK YOU, GOD, FOR EVERYONE WHO TAKES CARE OF ME. AMEN.

A happy ending

Naomi and Ruth arrived in Bethlehem. They were so poor that Ruth picked up leftover grain from the fields to make bread.

"Who's that stranger?" asked the farmer Boaz.

DEAR GOD, THANK YOU FOR MY LOVING FAMILY. AMEN.

"That's Ruth. She takes good care of Naomi," the farmworkers replied.

Why do you think Boaz wanted to marry Ruth?

"Then drop extra grain for Ruth," Boaz said kindly. Boaz decided to marry Ruth and they soon had a little boy. Now Naomi was very happy.

God answers a prayer

Hannah longed for a baby!
One day, she visited God's
house with her husband.
Hannah felt so sad.

"Please God," she cried, "send me a baby. I promise I'll give him back to you."

Eli, the priest, heard her. "May God answer your prayer!" he said. And God did!

Hannah called her baby Samuel.

Do you think the priest was a good man? Why?

THANK YOU, GOD, FOR LISTENING WHEN WE FEEL SAD. AMEN.

God calls Samuel

Hannah kept her promise.
She took Samuel to live with Eli,
the priest, at God's house.

One night, Samuel heard a voice:
"Samuel!"
He ran to Eli.
"I didn't call," Eli said.
"Go back to bed."

Three times Samuel heard the voice and three times he ran to Eli.

Then Eli said, "It's God's voice. Next time he calls, say, 'I'm listening.'"

God called again and Samuel listened to God's message.

How did Eli help Samuel?

DEAR GOD, HELP ME TO LISTEN WHEN YOU SPEAK TO ME. AMEN.

King of Israel

Samuel gave God's messages to the Israelites.
But they wanted a king instead.

"I will choose their king," God told Samuel.

One day, a young man called Saul arrived.
"My father's donkeys ran away," he told Samuel.

"I can't find them anywhere.
Can you help me?"

"Don't worry, your donkeys
have been found," Samuel said.
"God has chosen you to
be king of Israel!"

Saul disobeys God

One day, the Israelites were getting ready for battle.

PLEASE, GOD, HELP ME LEARN HOW TO WAIT. AMEN.

"Wait for me to pray before you fight," Samuel told King Saul. King Saul waited and waited. Finally, he decided to say the prayers himself.

When have you found it hard to wait for something?

Just then, Samuel came back.

"Why didn't you wait?" Samuel asked sadly. "Because you won't obey God, he is going to choose another king."

A new king

"Go and see Jesse," God told Samuel. "I have chosen one of his sons to be king." Jesse's eldest son was handsome. "He looks like a king!" thought Samuel.
But God whispered,
"No! Not this one."

THANK YOU, GOD, FOR LOVING US
WHATEVER WE LOOK LIKE. AMEN.

Samuel saw six more sons. But each time God said, "No!"

"Have you another son?" Samuel asked.

"Only young David," Jesse replied. "He's looking after my sheep."

When David arrived, God told Samuel, "He is the one! My chosen king!"

Do you think Samuel was surprised by God's choice of king? Why?

David and Goliath

David's brothers were in Saul's army. David was visiting them when the huge Philistine soldier, Goliath, bellowed, "Israelites, choose a man to fight me!"

The Israelites were terrified.

PLEASE, GOD, HELP US TO STAND UP FOR WHAT IS RIGHT. AMEN.

"I'll fight him!" said David, taking just his shepherd's sling and five stones.

"I'll feed you to the birds!" roared Goliath.

"I fight with God's strength!" David shouted.

He aimed. The stone from his sling hit Goliath's skull . . . crack! Goliath crashed to the ground.

Would you have wanted to fight the giant? Why?

David and Jonathan

Saul invited David to live in his palace. Whenever Saul was miserable, David would sing and play his harp to cheer him up.

David and Jonathan, Saul's son, became great friends. But Saul grew jealous of David.

One day, Saul hurled his spear at David. David dodged just in time!

THANK YOU, GOD, FOR BEST FRIENDS.
AMEN.

Saul chases David

When Saul discovered David had gone, he chased him. One night David and his nephew, Abishai, crept up on Saul and his soldiers as they slept. "Kill Saul now!" Abishai whispered.

DEAR GOD, PLEASE HELP ME TO FOLLOW YOU EVEN WHEN OTHERS WON'T. AMEN.

"Never!" David replied. "God would not want that. We'll take Saul's spear and water jug instead!"

When Saul discovered that David had taken his spear and jug but had not hurt him, he promised to stop chasing David.

Why did David choose not to hurt Saul?

David becomes king

One day, Saul and Jonathan died in battle and David became king.

"Jonathan is dead," David said sadly. "I must look after his family."

"Then take care of his son Mephibosheth," a servant said. "He can't walk."

How did David repay Jonathan's kindness?

So David invited Jonathan's son to the palace. "Welcome, Mephibosheth," he said.

Come and live here and have dinner with me every day."

THANK YOU, GOD, FOR KIND PEOPLE. AMEN.

Wise Solomon

When David died, his son Solomon became king. Solomon asked God to help him rule well. God made him wise.

DEAR GOD, GIVE US WISE PARENTS AND TEACHERS. AMEN.

One day, two mothers
arrived with a baby.

"He's my baby!"
the first woman cried.

"No! He's mine,"
the other shouted.

"Cut the baby in two,"
ordered Solomon, "and
give each mother half!"

"No!" cried the first
woman. "Don't hurt him!
Let her have him!"

"Take the baby," Solomon
told the first woman, "for
you are the real mother."

How did
Solomon know
who the real
mother was?

A temple for God

God made Solomon rich as well as wise. Solomon began to build a splendid home for God – the temple.

Thousands of builders got busy with fine wood and huge stones. Inside, in God's special room, even the floor was paved with gold!

Finally it was finished. Everyone celebrated. God promised to listen to his people when they prayed to him there.

THANK YOU, GOD, FOR LISTENING TO US WHEREVER WE ARE. AMEN.

Elijah and the bad king

Some kings of Israel were bad. King Ahab and his wicked queen, Jezebel, prayed to false gods and killed many of God's friends.

One day, God's friend Elijah brought Ahab a message.

"I serve the true God. There will be no rain until I say so!"

What Elijah said came true. Plants and animals began to die. Everyone was hungry. But God looked after Elijah.

How do we know that Elijah was serving the one true God?

DEAR GOD, PLEASE LOOK AFTER ME. AMEN.

The real God

THANK YOU, GOD, FOR BEING THE ONE AND ONLY REAL GOD. AMEN.

How does God help those who believe and trust in his love?

"Bring the servants of the false god Baal to Mount Carmel," Elijah told Ahab.

"We'll prove who's the real God."

"Build a fire with wood," Elijah told Baal's followers. "Now ask Baal to light it."

They prayed and prayed but nothing happened!

Elijah poured water over his wood. Then he prayed: "Please, God, send fire!"

At once, fire streaked down and set Elijah's wood alight. "Our God is the real God!" shouted the Israelites.

Elijah and Elisha

Jezebel was furious.
She wanted to kill Elijah.
But God kept him safe.

"Find Elisha," God told
Elijah. "He'll help you. He
will be my messenger too."

DEAR GOD, THANK YOU FOR BEING THERE
FOR ME WHEN I FEEL SCARED. AMEN.

One day, Elijah and Elisha were walking together, when they heard a rushing noise. Suddenly a chariot of fire, drawn by fiery horses, swooped down between them.

A great wind whirled Elijah off his feet. He was lifted up, up, and away—until Elisha could see him no more.

How do you think Elijah and Elisha would have felt when they saw the chariot?

One bottle of oil

A widow came to Elisha. "Help me!" she sobbed. "They're taking my sons away because I owe money."

THANK YOU, GOD, FOR LOOKING AFTER ME AND MY FAMILY. AMEN.

"What have you got at home?" Elisha asked.

"One small bottle of oil," she said.

"Borrow lots more bottles and fill them with your oil," Elisha said.

The boys fetched bottles and their mother poured and poured ... but the oil didn't run out until every borrowed bottle was full!

"Now sell the oil to pay your debt," said kind Elisha.

How did God help save the widow's sons?

Naaman is healed

Naaman, chief of the Syrian army, had a terrible skin disease. His young Israelite servant girl said, "Go to Elisha—God's messenger in Israel—he will make you better."

THANK YOU, GOD, FOR THE
MIRACLES YOU PERFORM. AMEN.

How did God show himself and his powers in the river Jordan?

"Wash seven times in the river Jordan," Elisha told Naaman.

"I can wash in cleaner rivers back home!" Naaman shouted angrily.

"Please do as Elisha says!" his soldiers pleaded.

So Naaman dipped in the river seven times—and his skin was smooth again!

"Your God is the real God!" Naaman told Elisha.

King Joash

After King Ahaziah died, his mother Athaliah, killed all the royal children to become queen! But baby Joash was rescued by his aunt. She hid him in God's temple.

When Joash was seven, the priest, Jehoiada, invited the people to the temple. He led Joash out, placed a crown on his head and gave him a copy of God's Law. Everyone cheered, "Long live King Joash!"

Athaliah was furious. Now Joash was God's king.

Do you think Joash's aunt was brave? Why?

DEAR GOD, PLEASE HELP ME TO FOLLOW YOU EVEN THOUGH I AM YOUNG. AMEN.

Jonah and the big fish

God told Jonah, "Go to the people of Nineveh. Tell them to stop being wicked."

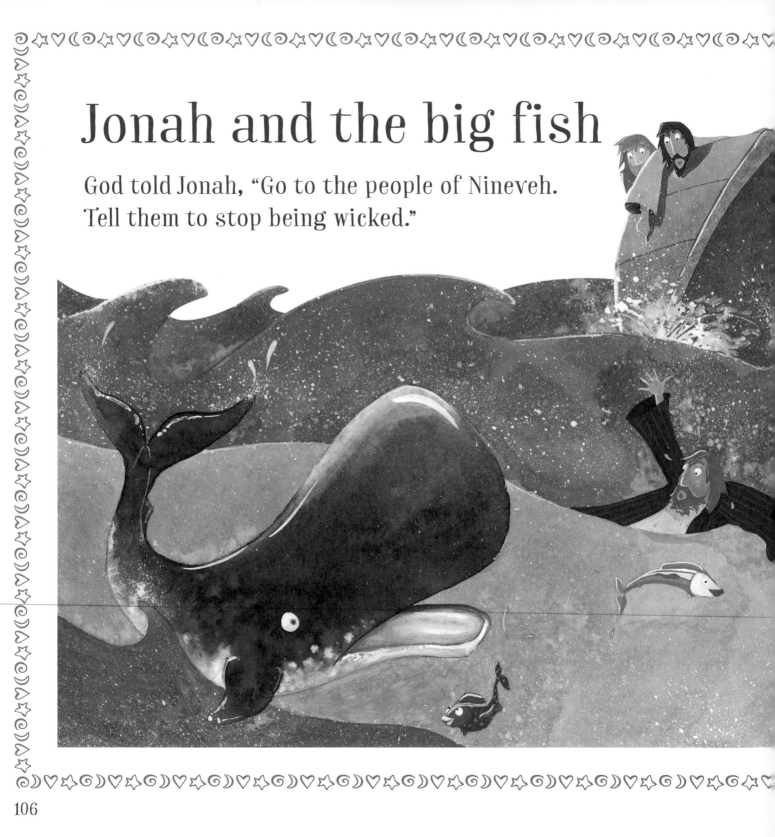

Jonah didn't want to go. He ran away and went to sea.
But God sent a strong wind to whip up the waves.

"We're going to sink!" cried the sailors.
"It's my fault!" Jonah said. "I ran away from God.
Throw me in the sea, and the storm will stop."

The sailors threw Jonah overboard
and the sea grew calm.

Why did Jonah
ask to be thrown
in the sea?

HELP ME, GOD, TO DO WHAT I'M TOLD.
AMEN.

God forgives

As Jonah sank beneath the waves, a big fish swam by and swallowed him up. Inside the fish Jonah prayed, "Please help me, God!"

God listened. He told the fish to spit Jonah out on the beach.

So Jonah went to Nineveh. The people listened to him. They promised to stop being wicked. "I forgive them," God told Jonah. But Jonah was angry. He did not want God to forgive his enemies.

Is it easy or hard to forgive our enemies? Why?

THANK YOU, GOD, FOR FORGIVING ME WHEN I'M TRULY SORRY. AMEN.

A lost book is found

God's temple in Jerusalem was falling to bits, so King Josiah sent builders and decorators to mend it.

There they found the lost copy of God's Law. A servant read it to King Josiah. He burst into tears.

"We haven't obeyed God!" he cried.

God sent Josiah a message: "There will be trouble later, but not for you, Josiah. I know you love me!"

Why is the Bible an important book?

THANK YOU, GOD, FOR YOUR TEACHINGS AND YOUR WORDS. AMEN.

Jeremiah is rescued

After good King Josiah there were more bad kings. God's messenger, Jeremiah, warned them that their enemies would fight them and win if they kept disobeying God.

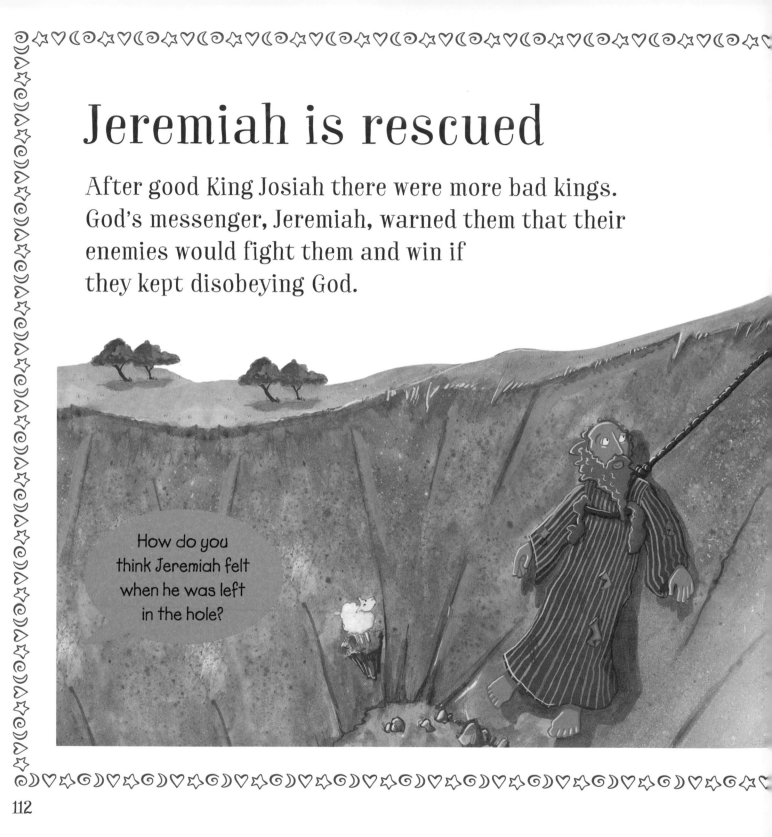

How do you think Jeremiah felt when he was left in the hole?

The leaders got angry—they threw
Jeremiah into a deep, muddy hole.
Ebedmelech went to the king.
"Your Majesty! Don't let Jeremiah die!"

"Go and rescue him!" ordered the king.
So Ebedmelech and his helpers rushed
off to pull Jeremiah up to safety.

PLEASE, GOD, HELP ME TO SPEAK
UP FOR YOU. AMEN.

Leaving Jerusalem

No one listened to Jeremiah's messages from God. Then Nebuchadnezzar—mighty king of Babylonia—brought his army to attack Jerusalem.

They stole the temple treasure and marched the people off to Babylonia.

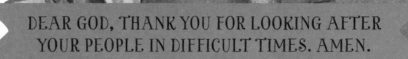

DEAR GOD, THANK YOU FOR LOOKING AFTER YOUR PEOPLE IN DIFFICULT TIMES. AMEN.

"Burn the city!" Nebuchadnezzar ordered. How sad God's people were as they left the city and the land God had given them!

How do you think God's people felt when they had to leave?

Daniel

Israel's cleverest young men were taken to Nebuchadnezzar's palace. "Eat the food the king sends you," the chief servant ordered.
But Daniel, Shadrach, Meshach, and Abednego knew that meant obeying the king rather than God.

PLEASE, GOD, HELP ME TO OBEY YOU.
AMEN.

"Give us vegetables and water for ten days," Daniel begged. The servant agreed.

After ten days they looked fit and healthy.

"These men are the best!" Nebuchadnezzar said. "They will help me rule."

Is it better to obey God or a king? Why?

Saved from the fire

"Bow down to my wonderful gold statue!" Nebuchadnezzar ordered. Everyone bowed down except Shadrach, Meshach, and Abednego.

"Bow down!" shouted Nebuchadnezzar. "Or I'll throw you into the fire!"

Were Shadrach, Meshach, and Abednego brave men? Why?

"We bow only to God!" the friends replied bravely.

So Nebuchadnezzar's soldiers threw them into the flames. Suddenly Nebuchadnezzar gasped: "We threw three men in, but there are four walking about in the fire! Their God has sent his angel to keep them safe!"

THANK YOU, GOD, FOR ANGELS
WHO LOOK AFTER US. AMEN.

Daniel and the lions

The new king liked Daniel. This made people jealous. "Order everyone to pray to you alone— or be thrown to the lions," they told the king.

THANK YOU, GOD, FOR KEEPING DANIEL SAFE. AMEN.

"Daniel is still praying to God!" said his enemies. So the king's soldiers threw Daniel into the lions' pit.

The king lay awake worrying. The next morning, he shouted, "Daniel! Did God save you?"

"Yes!" Daniel replied. "My God closed the lions' mouths! I'm safe!"

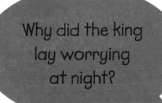

Why did the king lay worrying at night?

Queen Esther

PLEASE, GOD, HELP ME TO DO
THE RIGHT THING. AMEN.

Why did God make Esther queen?

"I want a queen," said the king of Persia. "Bring me the most beautiful girls in the kingdom."

The king chose Esther. But he did not know that Esther and her cousin, Mordecai, were Jews. Haman hated Mordecai, so he said to the king, "Let's kill those Jews from Israel."

The king agreed. Mordecai sent Esther a secret message:

"Help us!" he begged. "God made you queen to save your people."

Esther saves the Jews

"I will help," Esther told Mordecai. "Pray that the king will not be angry!"

Then, trembling, she went to the king. He welcomed her.

"Please come to dinner—and bring Haman, your chief advisor," Esther said.

After dinner Esther said, "Your Majesty, an enemy wants to kill me and my people!"

Do you think the king made the right decision in the end?

"Who is he?" the king asked.
Esther pointed to Haman.

"Take him away!" the king ordered.
"Mordecai will take his place."

PLEASE HELP ME, GOD, TO
NOT BE ANGRY. AMEN.

Rebuilding Jerusalem

After many years, the Jewish people came home, just as God had promised. Jerusalem was in ruins. So the people began rebuilding the temple.

Ezra, the priest, helped them finish it and taught them God's Word.

"Now let's rebuild the city wall," said Nehemiah. "God will help us!" So the people worked together, each family mending a part of the wall.

Why is it important to work together?

DEAR GOD, PLEASE HELP ME TO BE PATIENT. AMEN.

Give thanks to God

At last the wall was finished! Nehemiah called everyone to celebrate. Two groups of singers and musicians marched right around Jerusalem. The people sang, played their instruments, danced, and thanked God.

What were the people celebrating?

They all met up again at the temple. Everyone was happy because God had kept his promise.

The people of Israel had come home!

THANK YOU, GOD, FOR KEEPING YOUR PROMISE TO YOUR PEOPLE. AMEN.

New Testament Stories

An angel visits Mary	132	The sick girl	172	A special meal	214
Mary visits Elizabeth	134	Jesus and the blind man	174	Jesus is taken prisoner	216
A special message	136	Food for everyone	176	Peter lets Jesus down	218
Jesus is born	138	Jesus walks on water	178	Jesus is left to die	220
The shepherds	140	God talks to Jesus	180	A sad day	222
A promise fulfilled	142	The kind stranger	182	Jesus is alive!	224
The wise men	144	Martha and Mary	184	A surprise	226
Leaving for Egypt	146	A prayer to God	186	Tell everyone!	228
Jesus in the temple	148	Saying thank you	188	Thomas believes	230
John baptizes Jesus	150	The party	190	Jesus goes to Heaven	232
A test for Jesus	152	The lost sheep	192	The Holy Spirit	234
Andrew meets Jesus	154	Coming home	194	A man walks again	236
Peter goes fishing	156	Please forgive me!	196	An important man	238
Water into wine	158	Jesus gives new life	198	Jesus speaks to Paul	240
Walking again	160	Jesus and the children	200	God rescues Peter	242
A wise man and a		Zacchaeus changes	202	Friends of Jesus	244
foolish man	162	Expensive perfume	204	Paul is taken prisoner	246
The trusting soldier	164	Entering Jerusalem	206	God keeps his promise	248
Buried treasure	166	Being ready	208	Letters from Paul	250
The story of the seeds	168	Jesus is angry	210	A new heaven and earth	252
Jesus calms the storm	170	Washing feet	212	Index	254

An angel visits Mary

One day, God sent the angel
Gabriel to see Mary.
"Mary, don't be afraid,
God is pleased with you,"
Gabriel said. "You are
going to have a baby.
Call him Jesus. He will
be a great king."
Mary looked puzzled.

How did God let Mary know about the baby?

"The baby will be God's Son," Gabriel explained.

"I will do whatever God wants," Mary replied.

THANK YOU, GOD, THAT MARY WAS GLAD TO DO WHAT YOU ASKED. AMEN.

Mary visits Elizabeth

Mary couldn't wait to tell her cousin Elizabeth the news. She left home and hurried off. "Elizabeth!" she called, running to the house.

DEAR GOD, HELP ME TO REMEMBER TO THANK YOU, JUST LIKE MARY DID. AMEN.

Elizabeth hugged her.
"Mary! How wonderful! As soon as I heard you I knew that God had chosen you to be the mother of his promised king!"

Mary was so happy she sang "thank you" to God.

What can you say thank you to God for?

A special message

Joseph wanted to marry Mary. When he heard about Mary's baby he was worried.

That night, God's angel gave Joseph a special message.

DEAR GOD, HELP ME TO BE LIKE JOSEPH AND LISTEN TO WHAT YOU SAY. AMEN.

"Joseph, don't worry!" the angel said. "God wants you to marry Mary."

Do you think Joseph was happy to get the angel's message? Why?

"Her baby has been made by God's Holy Spirit. Call him Jesus. One day, he will rescue God's people." So Joseph married Mary.

Jesus is born

Bethlehem was busy. Mary and Joseph had traveled all the way from Nazareth. They needed somewhere to sleep, but all the inns were full.

At last Joseph found somewhere warm and dry– a stable! That night, Jesus was born. Mary wrapped him up warmly and laid him to sleep in the hay.

The shepherds

Shepherds were looking after their sheep when an angel appeared. God's dazzling light shone around.

How would you react if an angel appeared?

DEAR GOD, THANK YOU FOR SENDING YOUR ANGELS WITH THE GOOD NEWS ABOUT JESUS. AMEN.

"Don't be afraid!" said the angel. "I have good news! God's special king has been born in Bethlehem. You will find him lying in a manger."

Suddenly, the sky was filled with angels singing to God. The shepherds ran to Bethlehem. They were so happy when they found Jesus!

A promise fulfilled

One day, Mary and Joseph took baby Jesus to the temple. There they met an old man called Simeon.

Simeon had loved God all his life. He took Jesus gently in his arms.

"I'm so happy today!" he said. "Thank you, God, for keeping your promise and letting me see the king who will rescue us all."

Why was Simeon so happy?

DEAR GOD, THANK YOU FOR SENDING JESUS TO RESCUE US. AMEN.

The wise men

Far away in the East, some wise men saw a bright new star. "How wonderful!" they cried. "A great king has been born! Let's go and worship him!"

So they followed the star until it stopped over a house in Bethlehem.

What did the wise men think the star was a sign of?

The wise men were so happy to see Jesus.
They bowed down low and gave him precious
gifts—gold, frankincense, and myrrh.

THANK YOU, GOD, FOR MAKING THE STARS, ESPECIALLY
THE ONE THAT LED THE WISE MEN TO JESUS. AMEN.

Leaving for Egypt

Do you think it would have been scary escaping to Egypt?

DEAR GOD, YOU KEPT JESUS AND HIS FAMILY SAFE. PLEASE KEEP MY FAMILY SAFE, TOO. AMEN.

After the wise men had gone, Joseph saw an angel in his dreams.

"Joseph! Get up!" said the angel. "Hurry! Cruel King Herod wants to hurt Jesus. Go to Egypt. You will all be safe there. I will tell you when to come back."

Joseph leaped out of bed. He woke Mary and Jesus. They packed their bags and left at once.

After King Herod died, an angel told Joseph it was safe to return home.

Jesus in the temple

Mary, Joseph, and Jesus had been worshiping God in Jerusalem. They were traveling home to Nazareth.

"Have you seen Jesus?" Mary asked. Joseph shook his head. Oh no! Jesus had been left behind. Mary and Joseph rushed back to Jerusalem. They found Jesus in the temple.

"I've been here in my Father's house," said Jesus.

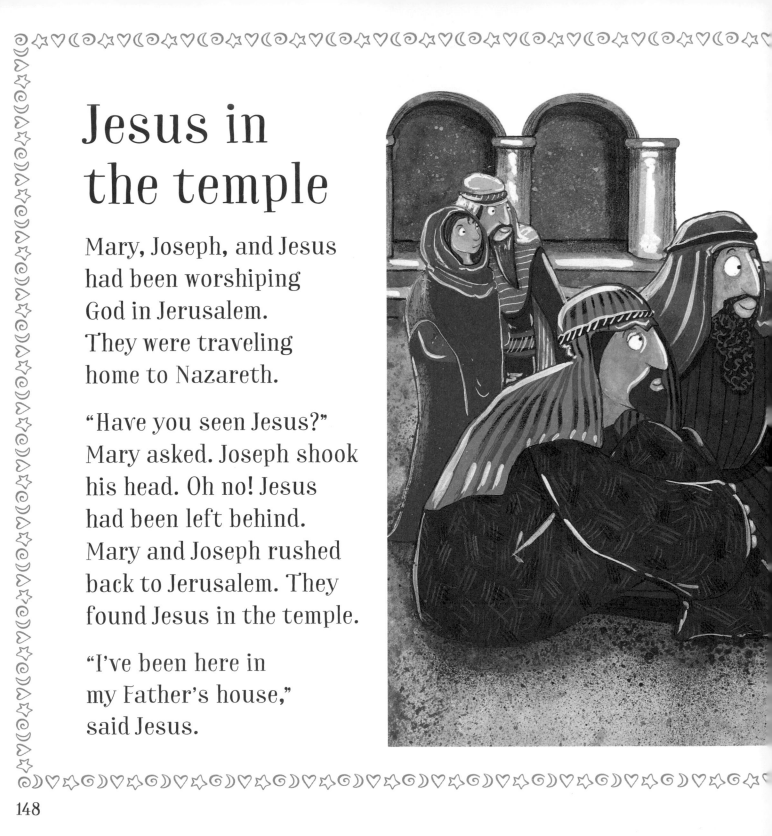

John baptizes Jesus

"Come back to God!" John shouted. "Say you are sorry and get baptized in the water so that God will forgive you and make you clean inside and out!"

How do people get baptized in your church?

DEAR GOD, I'VE DONE WRONG THINGS. I'M SORRY.
I'M GLAD THAT YOU MAKE ME CLEAN INSIDE. AMEN.

The people did what John told them. Jesus was good, but he came to be baptized, too. He always did what God wanted.

When Jesus came out of the water, God said, "You are my own dear Son. I am pleased with you!"

A test for Jesus

Jesus went into the desert to get ready to do God's work. God's enemy, the devil, came to trick Jesus. "I'll give you the whole world, if you bow down to me," he said.

"No!" said Jesus. "God has told everyone to bow down and serve no one else but him." Jesus chose to listen to God, not the devil, so the devil left.

DEAR GOD, PLEASE HELP ME BE LIKE JESUS AND DO WHAT YOU WANT. AMEN.

Andrew meets Jesus

One day, Andrew and his friend followed Jesus. "Where do you live?" Andrew called out. "Come and see!" said Jesus.

So they went to Jesus' house and talked with him all afternoon. Then Andrew rushed to find his brother. "Peter!" he said, "Come and meet Jesus, he's the king God promised us!"

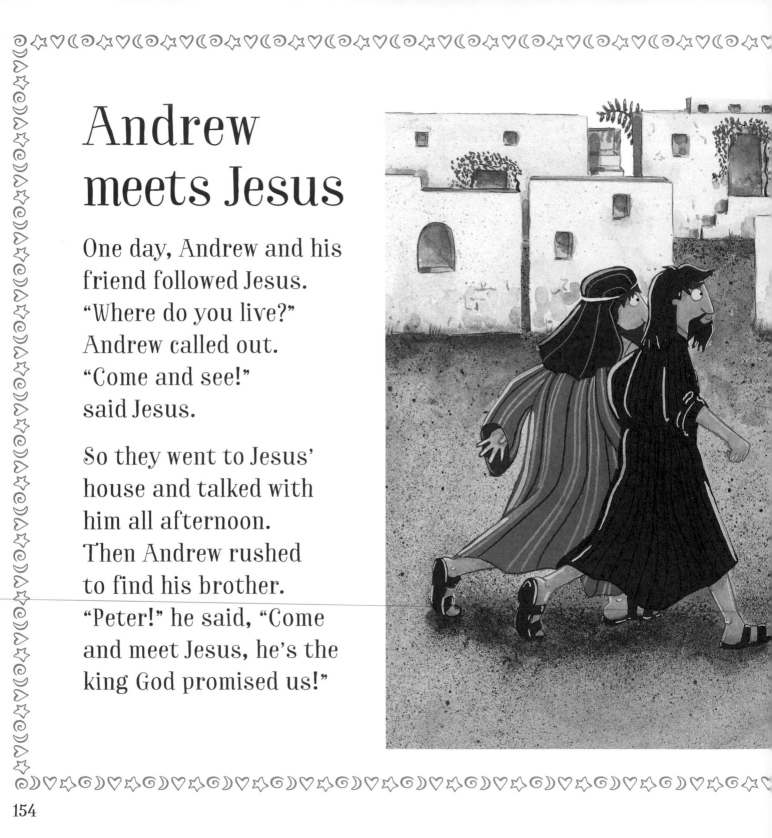

Peter goes fishing

Jesus was at the lake telling people about God. He climbed into Peter's boat.

"Let's go fishing!" he said. "I've been fishing. I didn't catch anything," Peter replied. But he did what Jesus said.

Suddenly the nets were bursting with wriggling fish. Peter was amazed.

DEAR GOD, PLEASE HELP ME TO DO WHAT YOU SAY. AMEN.

"Peter, come with me and we'll go fishing for people!" Jesus said. So Peter left his boat and followed Jesus.

Do you think Peter found it hard to leave his home and job?

DEAR GOD, YOU DO AMAZING THINGS.
YOU ARE WONDERFUL! AMEN.

Why did Mary tell Jesus that the wine had run out?

Water into wine

Mary and Jesus were at a wedding. Mary was worried. "Jesus, there's no more wine!"

"Fill these big jars with water," Jesus told the servants. "Then give some to the man in charge."

When the servants did what Jesus told them, they were amazed. Jesus had turned ordinary water into the very best wine!

Walking again

"Jesus will help you walk again," said the men as they carried their friend to Jesus' house. The house was too crowded.

THANK YOU, DEAR GOD, FOR LOOKING AFTER PEOPLE WHO ARE UNWELL. AMEN.

The men cut a hole in the roof and lowered their friend down.

Jesus smiled and said to the man, "I forgive you. Now get up and walk home."

To everyone's amazement, the man stood up and began to walk!

Why were the people amazed?

A wise man and a foolish man

PLEASE GOD, HELP ME TO MAKE
GOOD DECISIONS. AMEN.

One day, Jesus told a story:

There was once a foolish man who built his house on the sand. But the wise man built his house on the rock.

The wind shook the houses. The rain poured down, the floods rose. The house on the sand fell... CRASH! But the wise man was safe.

"If you do what I tell you," said Jesus, "you will be safe too!"

What can we learn from the wise man, and from the foolish man?

The trusting soldier

An important soldier came to see Jesus.
"My servant is very ill!" he said.

DEAR GOD, THE SOLDIER TRUSTED JESUS.
HELP ME TO TRUST JESUS, TOO. AMEN.

"I'll come and make him well," said Jesus.
"You don't need to come to my house," the soldier said.
"Just give the order and my servant will get better."
"I'm pleased you trust me so much," said Jesus.
"Go home, your servant is well now."

What did Jesus like about the soldier?

Buried treasure

"When you find God's kingdom, you will never let it go," Jesus said to his friends. And he told them this story:

The man gave up things to buy the field. What do we give up to go to heaven?

166

A man was digging in a field when he found treasure.
"If I buy this field, the treasure will be mine!" he thought.
So he sold everything he had and he bought the field.
He was so happy—now the treasure was his forever!

GOD, YOU ARE THE BEST
TREASURE OF ALL. AMEN.

The story of the seeds

HELP ME TO LISTEN, GOD. I WANT TO GROW
TO BE GOOD LIKE YOU. AMEN.

How are God's words like the seeds in this story?

"If you listen to me," said Jesus, "you'll be like the good soil in this story."

A farmer sowed his seeds. Some seeds fell on the path. The birds gobbled them up.

The seeds among the stones grew quickly, but they dried up in the hot sun.

Other seeds grew well until the weeds got in their way.

The seeds on the good soil grew into tall, healthy plants.

Jesus calms the storm

It had been a busy day. Jesus was fast asleep
in his friends' boat. Suddenly a wild
wind whipped up the waves.
They came crashing
over the boat.

DEAR JESUS, THANK YOU FOR HELPING
YOUR FRIENDS IN THE STORM. AMEN.

"Wake up, Jesus!" his friends shouted. "The boat is sinking!" Jesus got up. "Waves! Calm down!" he ordered. "Wind, be quiet!"

Why did Jesus' followers think this was such a big miracle?

At once all was safe and still. Jesus' friends were amazed. "Even the wind and waves do what Jesus says!"

The sick girl

Jairus' daughter was very ill. "Jesus, please make her better!" he begged.

Just then his servant ran up. "Your daughter is dead," he said sadly.

"Trust me, Jairus," Jesus said gently, "your little girl will get well."

At Jairus' house everyone was crying. The girl was lying pale and still.

"Little girl," Jesus said, taking her hand, "get up!" She opened her eyes and stood up—alive and well.

Has God ever helped you to feel better?

DEAR GOD, THANK YOU FOR HELPING AND HEALING PEOPLE. AMEN.

Jesus and the blind men

As Jesus left Jairus' house two blind men shouted out, "Jesus, be kind and help us!"

"Do you believe I can make you better?" Jesus asked.

"Oh yes!" they replied.

DEAR GOD, PLEASE HELP ME TO HAVE FAITH LIKE THE TWO BLIND MEN. AMEN.

"Then because you believe in me, it will happen," said Jesus as he reached out and touched their eyes.

At once the men could see!

What happened when the blind men believed in Jesus?

Food for everyone

The crowd had listened to Jesus all day.

"They're hungry," said Jesus.

"Let's give them some food."

"We don't have enough money!" his friends replied.

"This boy has five little loaves and two fish," said Andrew.

Jesus took the loaves and the fish and thanked God for them. Then he handed out the food. And everyone had plenty to eat!

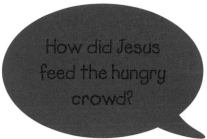

How did Jesus feed the hungry crowd?

THANK YOU, GOD, FOR ALL OUR FOOD. AMEN.

Jesus walks on water

One evening Jesus went away to pray.
His friends set off across the lake.
They puffed and panted as they rowed.

Suddenly they saw someone walking on the water toward them. "It's a ghost!" they screamed.

"Don't be scared," said the man, climbing into their boat. "It's me, Jesus!" The friends were amazed. It was Jesus!

Why do you think Jesus could walk on water?

JESUS, NO ONE ELSE CAN WALK ON WATER. YOU ARE TRULY SPECIAL. AMEN.

God talks to Jesus

Jesus took Peter, James, and John up a mountain to pray. Jesus grew brighter and brighter until even his clothes shone dazzling white. The friends were amazed. They saw Moses and Elijah, two of God's prophets from long ago, talking with Jesus!

DEAR GOD, PLEASE HELP ME TO
LISTEN TO JESUS. AMEN.

The kind stranger

Jesus told another story: A man was lying badly hurt by the side of the road. A priest came along. But he did not help, he just walked away!

Then another important man walked by. But he did not stop to help either.

At last, a kind stranger stopped. He bandaged the man, took him to an inn, and looked after him there. "Be kind like the stranger in this story," said Jesus.

How was the stranger a better person than the important man?

PLEASE, GOD, HELP ME TO
BE KIND TO OTHERS. AMEN.

Martha and Mary

Jesus was at Martha and Mary's house. Mary sat down to listen to Jesus. But Martha rushed around getting the food ready.

Martha was upset. "Jesus!" she said. "I'm doing all the work by myself. Tell Mary to help me!"

"Oh, Martha," said Jesus gently, "Mary wants to be with me. She has chosen what is most important."

Why did Mary want to sit with Jesus?

DEAR GOD, PLEASE HELP ME TO SPEND MORE TIME CONCENTRATING ON JESUS. AMEN.

A prayer to God

"Jesus, teach us how to talk to God," his friends asked. So Jesus taught them this prayer:

Our Father in heaven, may everyone know and love you. Come and be our King.

Give us today the food we need. Forgive the bad things we do. Help us to forgive others, too.

When we want to do something bad, help us choose to do good instead.

Saying thank you

One day, Jesus met some men with a skin disease.
"Jesus, please make us better!" they called.

"Find the priest," Jesus said kindly,
"so he can see you are well again."

As the men set off, they saw that their skin was as good
as new! But only one of them rushed back to thank Jesus.

The party

"God invites people into his kingdom," Jesus said, "like the man who was getting ready for his party."

"The important people he had invited sent messages saying, 'We're sorry, we're too busy to come.'

"Then the man told his servants, 'Go! Find the people who are never invited to parties and bring them here.'

Soon the man's house was full of people having fun."

Why did Jesus invite other people to the party?

DEAR GOD, THANK YOU FOR INVITING US INTO YOUR KINGDOM. AMEN.

The lost sheep

Everyone crowded around as Jesus told this story about what God's kingdom is like:

There was once a shepherd who had one hundred sheep. One day, he discovered one was missing.

He searched up and down, near and far. Finally he found it. He was so happy that he carried it all the way home! "I've found my lost sheep!" he called to his friends. "Let's have a party!"

Like the shepherd in the story, God is happy when even one sinner turns back to him.

Why is this story good news for us when we make mistakes?

DEAR GOD, THANK YOU FOR HELPING THE SHEPHERD FIND HIS SHEEP. AMEN.

Coming home

There was once a son who left home. He soon spent his father's money.

"I'm hungry and unhappy," the young man thought. "I'll go back and tell my father I'm sorry."

As soon as his father saw him, he ran to hug him. "My son has come home!" he called to his servants. "Let's have a party!"

"God is so happy when we come home to him," Jesus said.

How is this story like the story of the lost sheep?

GOD, THANK YOU FOR LOVING US EVEN WHEN WE MAKE MISTAKES. AMEN.

Please forgive me!

Two men went to the temple
to pray. The first man said,
"God, I keep all your rules,
I don't cheat or steal
like that man there."

The second man stood
sadly at the back.
"I know I'm a bad
man, God." He prayed,
"Please forgive me."

"Guess which man God
was pleased with?" said
Jesus. "The one who
said he was sorry."

Where do you
go to pray?

DEAR GOD, PLEASE FORGIVE ME WHEN
I GET THINGS WRONG. AMEN.

Jesus gives new life

JESUS, YOU ARE GOOD AND POWERFUL. YOU HAVE DONE MANY WONDERFUL THINGS. AMEN.

Martha and Mary were very sad because their brother Lazarus had died.

"I can give new life," Jesus said to them. "Anyone who trusts me will never really die."

He went to the place where Lazarus was buried. "Move the stone away!" Jesus ordered.

"Lazarus, come out!" he called.

And to everyone's amazement, Lazarus walked out alive and well.

Jesus and the children

Some people brought their children to see Jesus.
Jesus' friends said, "Go away! Don't bother Jesus.
He's much too busy." Jesus was angry with them.

"Let the children come to me," he said. "Don't stop them. God wants children in his kingdom."

The children ran to Jesus' open arms. He hugged them and asked God to take special care of them.

If you were a child back then, would you have wanted to see Jesus?

DEAR GOD, THANK YOU FOR ALWAYS TAKING CARE OF ME. AMEN.

Zacchaeus changes

"I can't see Jesus over this crowd,"
thought Zacchaeus, so he climbed a tree.

Jesus walked by and looked up.
"Zacchaeus!" he said. "I'm
coming to your house today!"

The crowd gasped. Zacchaeus was a cheat; nobody liked him! Zacchaeus gasped. Could Jesus really want to be his friend?

Zacchaeus had a wonderful day with Jesus. And he promised not to cheat anyone again.

Why did Jesus visit Zacchaeus?

THANK YOU, GOD, FOR GETTING TO KNOW ME AND HELPING ME LEARN FROM YOU. AMEN.

Expensive perfume

As Jesus and his friends were eating, Mary poured
her precious bottle of perfume over Jesus' feet.
Then she wiped them gently with her long hair.
A wonderful, sweet smell filled the room.

"Mary should have sold that perfume and given the money to the poor," complained Judas. But Jesus was pleased with Mary. "Mary has done something very special for me," he said.

How did Mary honor Jesus?

DEAR GOD, THANK YOU FOR EVERYTHING THAT YOU DO. AMEN.

Entering Jerusalem

DEAR GOD, I WOULD LIKE TO SAY
THANK YOU FOR JESUS. AMEN.

On what day each year do we remember this event?

Jesus rode into Jerusalem on a young donkey. The people spread branches and cloaks on the ground— like a carpet for a king.

The crowds waved branches to welcome Jesus.

"Hooray for God's special king!" they cheered.

"Who is this man?" people asked.

"It's Jesus! God's messenger!" the crowds replied.

Being ready

"Be ready for God's kingdom," said Jesus, as he told this story:

There were ten bridesmaids who were waiting for the bridegroom to arrive. The wise girls took extra oil for their lamps. The foolish girls did not.

At midnight their lamps ran out of oil, so they went off to buy more. Suddenly, the bridegroom arrived. He took the wise bridesmaids to his wedding party. But the foolish bridesmaids missed out.

What lesson did the foolish girls learn?

DEAR GOD, PLEASE HELP ME TO
FOLLOW YOU EVERY DAY. AMEN.

Jesus is angry

God's temple was busy when Jesus arrived.
"Buy a lamb here," shouted some sellers.
"Doves for sale!" yelled others.

Jesus was very angry. There was so much
noise; no one could talk to God.

Why was Jesus angry with the sellers in the temple?

"God's house is a special place to pray," said Jesus, pushing over a stall piled high with money, "not somewhere to buy and sell and cheat!" Then he chased them all out of the temple.

DEAR GOD, THANK YOU FOR QUIET PLACES TO PRAY. AMEN.

Washing feet

One evening, during supper, Jesus got up, tied a towel around his waist, and began to wash his friends' feet. They were shocked—it was the servant's job to wash feet.

DEAR GOD, PLEASE HELP ME TO BE LOVING AND HELPFUL LIKE JESUS. AMEN.

"Jesus, you mustn't wash our feet," said Peter.
"I'm washing your feet because I love you," said Jesus.
"Now copy me. Love and help each other."

Why did Jesus choose to do a servant's job?

A special meal

Jesus was eating a special meal with his friends when he took some bread, thanked God, broke it in pieces, and handed it around.

"This is my body," he said. "I give it for you." Then he took a cup of wine, thanked God, and passed it around. "Drink this," he said. "I will die for many people because God has promised to forgive them."

Like Jesus, do you ever thank God before eating a meal?

THANK YOU, JESUS, FOR GIVING YOUR LIFE FOR EVERYONE. AMEN.

Jesus is taken prisoner

How did Jesus show bravery and loyalty to God in his prayers?

Jesus was praying in the garden. He was sad because he knew he was going to die soon.

"Father, don't let me die," he prayed. "But if dying is part of your plan then I will do what you want."

DEAR GOD, THANK YOU FOR LISTENING TO ME WHEN I FEEL SAD OR AFRAID. AMEN.

Suddenly Jesus' friend Judas arrived, leading a crowd of Jesus' enemies. He kissed Jesus. At once the soldiers surrounded Jesus and took him prisoner.

Peter lets Jesus down

DEAR GOD, PLEASE HELP ME WHEN IT'S HARD TO BE YOUR FRIEND. AMEN.

Could you own up to knowing Jesus if it might get you hurt?

Peter followed Jesus and the soldiers. "Aren't you Jesus' friend?" asked a servant girl. Peter shook his head, "No! I don't know him!"

Two more people asked if he knew Jesus. "No!" said Peter. "No!"

Suddenly a rooster crowed. Peter remembered that Jesus had said: "Before the rooster crows, you will say three times that you're not my friend." Peter burst into tears.

Jesus is left to die

Jesus' enemies took Jesus to Pilate, the Roman ruler.
Pilate asked Jesus lots of questions. Then he said,
"Jesus has not done anything wrong. I will let him go."
"NO!" the people shouted. "Kill Jesus! Nail him to a cross!"

JESUS, THANK YOU FOR LOVING EVERYONE
ENOUGH TO DIE TO SAVE THEM. AMEN.

So Pilate's soldiers nailed Jesus to a cross and left him to die. Jesus knew that he had done what God wanted.

"My work is finished!" he cried. Then he died.

How do you think Jesus' family and friends felt when he died?

A sad day

Jesus was dead. Nicodemus and Joseph of Arimathea had been afraid to say they were Jesus' friends.

DEAR GOD, THANK YOU FOR BEING THERE WHEN I AM SAD. AMEN.

But now they showed that they loved him.
They wrapped Jesus' body in cloth
with precious perfumes and carefully
put him in a new tomb.

How did Jesus' friends honor him after he died?

Together they rolled the heavy stone across the doorway. Then they walked sadly away.

Jesus is alive!

Two days later Mary Magdalene stood outside
Jesus' tomb. It was empty! Jesus' body was gone.

"Why are you
crying?" asked
a man standing
nearby.

"Have you taken
Jesus away?"
Mary sobbed.

"Mary!" said the man gently. Mary looked up.
It was Jesus! He smiled. "Go and tell my friends."

Mary ran all the way. She couldn't wait to tell them the good news–Jesus was ALIVE!

Why do you think Mary didn't recognize Jesus?

THANK YOU, GOD, FOR EASTER TIME. IT'S WONDERFUL THAT JESUS IS ALIVE! AMEN.

A surprise

Two of Jesus' friends met a man on their way home. "Jesus was killed three days ago," they told him, "but Mary says Jesus is alive again!"

Do you think Jesus' friends believed Mary?

"God promised this would happen to his special king," said the stranger. At supper time, the man thanked God for the bread, then gave it to the friends. Suddenly the friends knew—the stranger was Jesus. He really was alive!

DEAR GOD, HELP ME TO KNOW EVERY DAY
THAT JESUS IS ALIVE. AMEN.

The two friends ran back to Jerusalem. "We've seen Jesus!" they said to all of Jesus' friends.

Suddenly Jesus was there, too! Everyone stopped talking. "Don't be scared," Jesus said. "It's me. Touch me—I'm not a ghost!"

They were so happy to see Jesus alive again.

"Tell everyone everywhere about me," Jesus told them. "Because of me, they can be God's friends again."

Thomas believes

Thomas didn't believe Jesus was alive.
"When I have seen and touched Jesus for
myself, then I'll believe," he said.

A week later, Jesus came again.
"Thomas, look! Touch my hands and
feet. It really is me," Jesus said.

DEAR GOD, HELP ME TO BELIEVE IN YOU,
EVEN THOUGH I CAN'T SEE YOU. AMEN.

Thomas gazed at him. "My Lord and my God!" he said.

"Now you believe!" said Jesus. "God is pleased with people who believe even if they don't see me."

Why was Thomas amazed to see Jesus?

Jesus goes to heaven

DEAR JESUS, YOU ARE COMING BACK
ONE DAY. THAT'S SO EXCITING! AMEN.

Who do you think the men in white might have been?

"Wait in Jerusalem," Jesus told his friends. "God will send you His Holy Spirit. He will help you tell the whole world about me."

Then, before their eyes, Jesus was taken up to heaven.

Suddenly two men dressed in white appeared.

"Why are you standing here looking at the sky?" they asked. "Jesus will come back one day."

The Holy Spirit

Jesus' friends were praying when...whoosh!
A sound like a rushing wind roared through the house.

A flickering flame rested gently on each head. God's Holy Spirit had come to help them tell others about Jesus.

THANK YOU, GOD, FOR SENDING YOUR HOLY SPIRIT. AMEN.

When the people from other countries heard what God had done, they wanted to be Jesus' friends, too.

A man walks again

Peter and John were going to the temple.

"Please give me money!" begged a man who could not walk.

"I don't have any," Peter said kindly, "but I know Jesus, God's king. And Jesus tells you to walk!"

Right away the man's feet and legs were strong again—he could walk, run, and jump! "Thank you!" he shouted. "God is great!"

An important man

DEAR GOD, PLEASE HELP ME TO LISTEN TO THE HOLY SPIRIT, TOO. AMEN.

God's angel sent Philip to a dusty desert road. The chariot of an important African man rumbled by.

"Keep up with that chariot, Philip," said God's Holy Spirit.

Philip ran alongside. He heard the man reading God's book. "Do you understand it?" asked Philip. "No," sighed the man. "What does it mean?"

Philip explained that it was all about Jesus, and the man decided to become Jesus' friend too.

Jesus speaks to Paul

DEAR GOD, THANK YOU FOR YOUR POWER
TO MAKE PEOPLE WELL. AMEN.

How did Jesus get Paul to help spread his messages?

Paul did not believe that Jesus was God's special king. He hated Jesus' friends.

He set off to find them and put them in prison. FLASH! A bright light shone. Paul fell to the ground.

"Paul, why do you hate me and hurt me?" said a voice. "Who are you?" asked Paul. "I am Jesus!"

Paul was shocked. Jesus was alive! From that moment Paul became Jesus' friend.

"Go and tell everyone about me," Jesus said.

God rescues Peter

Peter was in prison. The soldiers guarded him night and day. One night an angel shook Peter awake. Peter's chains fell to the ground.

"Quick, put on your sandals," said the angel. "Follow me."

DEAR GOD, PLEASE WATCH OVER ME AND PROTECT ME. AMEN.

So Peter followed the angel past the guards, through the gate and into the street. Then the angel disappeared.

Peter blinked. It wasn't a dream – he really was free!

Have you ever dreamed about an angel?

Friends of Jesus

Paul traveled to many places telling people about Jesus. One night a man called to Paul in a dream, "Come to Macedonia! Help us!"

How did Paul help spread Jesus' message?

The next day Paul sailed to Macedonia.

THANK YOU, GOD, FOR ALL THE PEOPLE WHO TELL ME ABOUT JESUS. AMEN.

There he met Lydia, a rich woman, and her friends. He told them about Jesus. So Lydia and her friends became friends of Jesus too.

Paul is taken prisoner

One day, when Paul was at the temple, Jesus' enemies tried to kill him. "Paul tells lies!" they shouted.

Just then the Roman commander marched in. His soldiers stopped the people from hurting Paul.

THANK YOU, GOD, FOR BEING MY FRIEND, EVEN WHEN OTHERS ARE UNKIND. AMEN.

Did the commander do what the crowd wanted?

Paul explained that God wanted everyone to know Jesus was alive, but the crowd shouted, "NO! Get rid of Paul."
So the commander put Paul in prison.

God keeps his promise

"The Roman emperor must decide if I am right," Paul said. So the soldiers took Paul and set sail for Rome.

Before long, the ship was caught in a raging storm.

"Don't be afraid," said Paul. "God will keep us all safe."

As the ship broke up, everyone swam for the shore. At last they reached the land—cold, wet, but safe. God had kept his promise.

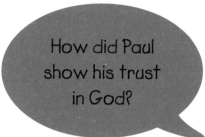

How did Paul show his trust in God?

THANK YOU, GOD. YOU ALWAYS KEEP YOUR PROMISES! AMEN.

Letters from Paul

Finally Paul and the soldiers arrived in Rome. Paul was still a prisoner, but he was allowed to write to all the people he had met on his travels. They had become friends of Jesus too.

They told Paul their problems and he wrote back to help them.

DEAR GOD, THANK YOU FOR HEAVEN
AND EARTH. AMEN.

Would you like to live in the new earth? Why?

A new heaven and earth

One day, John saw a man – strong, good, and shining bright. It was Jesus!

"Write to my friends," Jesus said. "Tell them that God is going to make a new heaven and a new earth where no one will be hurt or die! All God's friends will live with him forever."

Index

This index shows where to find some favorite Bible stories in this book and also shows groups of stories that link together.

The Old Testament

The New Testament

In the Beginning

The creation and fall	8–15
Noah's ark	18–21

God's Special People

Abraham	22–27
Jacob	28–32
Joseph	32–39
Moses	40–57

Brave People of God

Joshua	56–61
Gideon	62–63
Samson	64–67
Ruth	68–71

Prophets, Priests and Kings

Samuel	72–81
Saul	76–89
David	80–89
Solomon	90–93
Elijah	94–99
Elisha	98–103
Jonah	106–109

The Exile and Return

Leaving Jerusalem	114–115
Daniel and his friends	116–121
Esther	122–125
Rebuilding Jerusalem	126–129

The Christmas Story

An angel visits Mary	132–133
Jesus is born	138–139
The shepherds	140–141
The wise men	144–145
Leaving for Egypt	146–147

When Jesus Grew Up

John baptizes Jesus	150–151
A test for Jesus	152–153
God talks to Jesus	180–181
A prayer to God	186–187

Jesus and his Friends

Andrew meets Jesus	154–155
Martha and Mary	184–185
Jesus and the children	200–201
Zacchaeus changes	202–203

Jesus' Miracles

Water into wine	158–159
Walking again	160–161
The trusting soldier	164–165
Jesus calms the storm	170–171
The sick girl	172–173
Jesus and the blind men	174–175
Food for everyone	176–177
Jesus walks on water	178–179
Saying thank you	188–189
Jesus gives new life	198–199

Stories Jesus Told

A wise man and a foolish man	162–163
Buried treasure	166–167
The story of the seeds	168–169
The kind stranger	182–183
The party	190–191
The lost sheep	192–193
Coming home	194–195
Being ready	208–209

The Easter Story

Entering Jerusalem	206–207
A special meal	214–215
Jesus is taken prisoner	216–217
Jesus is left to die	220–221
Jesus is alive!	224–225

Jesus is Alive

A surprise	226–227
Thomas believes	230–231
Jesus goes to heaven	232–233

Jesus' Friends Share the Good News

The Holy Spirit	234–235
A man walks again	236–237
An important man	238–239
Jesus speaks to Paul	240–241
A new heaven and earth	252–253